FOREWORD

Obsessive Compulsive Disorder (OCD) is a common condition that, by
of the population. After long being regarded as rare in childhood recent evidence has shown this not to be the case, with up to half of those developing the condition in adulthood experiencing an onset of their symptoms in childhood. Isolated OCD symptoms are also now known to be very prevalent in children, with up to a quarter experiencing them at some point in their lives.

Longitudinal studies into the evolution of the disorder have also identified a pattern of subclinical OCD symptoms, typically starting in middle childhood, in those who go on to develop the illness later in life. However, the fact it frequently co-presents with a multitude of childhood anxieties coupled with the recognition among sufferers of the irrationality of obsessive thinking, can result in those affected enduring their symptoms in secret without access to early and effective intervention.

Drawing on her considerable experience of dealing with the condition and the insights she has gained through her own personal journey, Mrs Derrick has produced an excellent illustrated resource, replete with vignettes and practical tips, for families of children who may be experiencing the precursors or the early stages of an Obsessive Compulsive Disorder. It does a very good job of presenting the condition from the child's perspective, covers the basic principles of treatment, including 'externalising' symptoms as a means of increasing motivation as well as exposure and response prevention techniques, in a manner that makes sense to children and families.

We commend Mrs Derrick for her efforts and wish her every success in her mission to increase awareness and reduce stigma around mental health difficulties in children and young people.

Dr Krishna Menon MRCPsych, Consultant Child Psychiatrist and Clinical Director
Sian Carroll, Clinical Nurse Specialist
Cwm Taf Morgannwg University Health Board

Trixie the Treat Monster

First published in 2021 by

Panocub, an imprint of Panoma Press Ltd
48 St Vincent Drive, St Albans, Herts, AL1 5SJ, UK
info@panocub.com
www.panocub.com
info@panomapress.com
www.panomapress.com

Book illustrations by Glen Holman
Book layout by Neil Coe.

978-1-838144-61-6

A CIP catalogue record for this book is available from the British Library.

This book is available online and in bookstores.

Trixie loves her job.

Trixie helps children to magic away bad thoughts.

She's busy reading a new message on her screen, which says,

"URGENT MISSION. LEO NEEDS YOUR HELP."

Leo loves playing football. He is about to kick a penalty shot, when he stops.

First, he needs to count.

"ONE, TWO, THREE."

He's about to kick the ball again, but begins counting again, just in case.

"ONE, TWO, THREE."

Counting brings Leo luck.

It's his little secret, though.

Counting used to be such fun, but now he finds it miserable, because he needs to do it over and over, or he'll miss the shot.

Trixie is busy watching Leo on her screen.

"Hmm, looks like Hank is up to his tricks again," she thinks.

She presses the back arrow on her screen to investigate further.

"There it is!" she shouts with glee.

She’s studying an older image of Leo missing a shot at goal, while his friend Emily watches on.

Leo is looking very embarrassed and flushed.

“This is when Hank started playing his game,” she decides. “Here’s when Leo started counting.”

Trixie quickly presses the forward button to take her back to the present.

She can see Leo 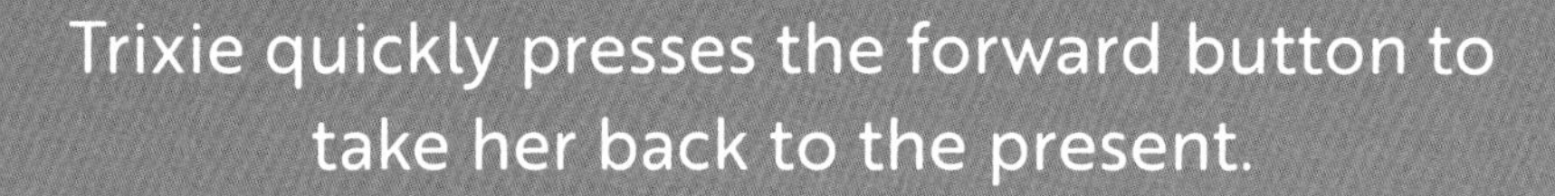

waiting to take his penalty shot.

The more nervous he gets, the more he counts,

"ONE, TWO, THREE ... ONE, TWO, THREE ... ONE, TWO, THREE."

Trixie is watching it all.

So is Hank, who is busy pressing his 'KEEP COUNTING' control.

"Hmm, time to put my plan into action," Trixie decides.

She presses the 'TREAT' control on her screen.

Leo is about to start counting again, when...

Ping!

An image of his favourite ice cream suddenly appears in his head.

Before he realises, he's kicked the ball into the net and everyone is cheering, including his friend Emily.

"That's strange," he thinks. "I didn't finish counting that time, but the ball still went in. That was lucky."

Hank, meanwhile, is confused.

His controls are jammed and all that he can see on his screen is an ice cream.

Trixie likes Hank, but she doesn't like the games that he plays.

Trixie likes fun games, but Hank prefers games that make people miserable. Trixie enjoys playing against Hank – and she likes to win.

Trouble is, **so does Hank!**

Hank is becoming frustrated.

He's pressing his controls, but nothing is happening.

He glances at the corner of his screen and sees Trixie, who is pressing her controls quicker than him.

"That's why my controls are jammed," he decides.

It’s penalty practice time again.

Leo hates penalty practice.

Taking a shot takes so long when he has to count so many times.

He thinks it’s silly, but he has to do it, just in case.

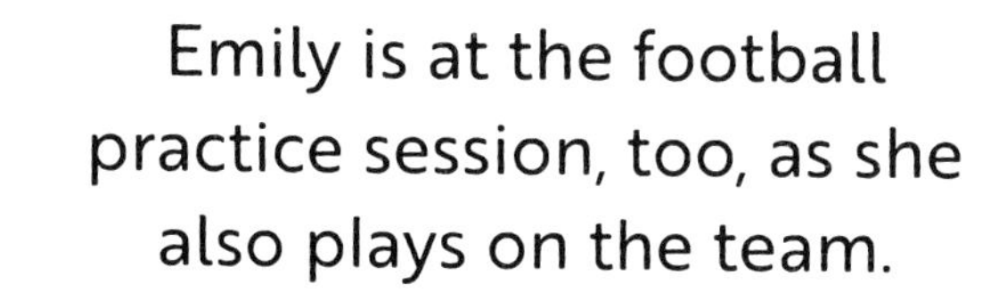

Emily is at the football practice session, too, as she also plays on the team.

She notices that Leo is taking longer to take his penalty shots.

She wonders what's wrong.

"I'll ask him later," she decides.

Trixie is deep in thought.

Hank is very clever with his games, so she knows that she needs to act quickly, if she wants to get ahead.

Too late. Leo has begun to count again.

"ONE, TWO, THREE."

Ping! 'CONTINUE COUNTING.'

Hank delivers his command.

Trixie has other ideas, and presses her controls.

Ping! 'DISPLAY PIZZA IMAGE.'

Just as Leo starts counting again, an image of his favourite pizza pings into his head... and he scores a goal!

The counting stops.

Trixie knows that Hank won't give up that easily, though.

She decides to enlist Emily to help her.

Ping! "LEO HAS A SECRET THAT HE NEEDS TO SHARE."

Trixie delivers a message direct to Emily.

Emily leads Leo to a bench and they sit down to chat.

"Is there anything worrying you, Leo?" she gently asks.

"No, why do you ask?" replies Leo.

"Because you seem really nervous before taking a penalty shot," Emily adds.

Leo really wants to confide in Emily, but he's embarrassed.

He quickly changes the conversation.

Trixie has other ideas, though.

She sends another message direct to Emily.

Ping! **"ASK HIM AGAIN WHAT'S WRONG."**

Leo is getting really anxious.

Hank is delighted and decides to continue with his game.

This time, it works perfectly.

Ping! 'COUNT ONE, TWO, THREE.'

Leo begins to count.

Ping! 'REPEAT.'

Leo is counting, over and over in his head.

Emily has noticed and is getting concerned.

"What are you thinking about right now, Leo?" she asks.

"Nothing," he continues.

Emily is not put off that easily.

"I get anxious about things, too, Leo," she continues.

Leo is wondering whether to confide in Emily, when...

Ping! Trixie delivers a new message to Emily.

"TELL LEO WHAT YOU WORRY ABOUT," she requests.

"Let's share what we worry about, Leo.
Here's my biggest fear," Emily responds.

"My biggest worry is that I will fall over in front of everyone in a football match," giggles Emily.

Leo is shocked as he thinks that Emily is fearless.

"How do you manage to keep it a secret?" Leo asks.

"That's easy," replies Emily. "When I'm worried, I think about something happy. What do you do?" she asks.

"I count."

Leo has replied before realising.

He feels embarrassed.

To his surprise, Emily simply replies,

"Gosh! Counting must be so tiring."

"Why don't you try thinking about something else instead of counting?" she offers.

"Like what?" asks Leo.

"Try thinking about your favourite treat. What if I buy you a slice of **pizza** if you don't count in the next match?"

Leo is shocked. He doesn't expect this reply.

No laughing, **no** making fun, **no** embarrassing comments.

Just the promise of a pizza from his best friend.

"That wasn't so bad," he thinks.

"It's a deal," Leo replies.

Trixie is jumping up and down with delight. She has been watching it all on her screen.

"This is all going to plan perfectly," she thinks.

She presses her home screen, which shows Hank looking very cross and frustrated.

It's match time again.

Leo is about to kick a penalty shot, just as Hank is pressing the **'COMMENCE COUNTING'** control.

Leo's urge to start counting begins again.

Trixie notices and quickly presses her **'TREAT'** control.

A pepperoni pizza pings into Leo's head while Emily is looking over, smiling.

THUMP! The ball hits the back of the net.

After the match, Emily buys Leo a pizza.

Trixie is delighted and Hank, begrudgingly, admits defeat.

ACKNOWLEDGEMENTS

This book is dedicated to all of the people who have inspired me to write my Mind Monsters books and to be brave enough to share them with the outside world.

I'd like to especially thank my mum and dad and my husband, Roy, for supporting and motivating me, along with my family and friends. There are too many of you to individually name, but you know who you are.

A big thank you to Glen, my illustrator, and to everyone at Panocub, especially Mindy and Emma, for all your patience and support in helping me to get my books published and raise awareness of this debilitating illness.

I also want to give a MASSIVE thanks to the CITT medical team within CAMHS, especially Dr Menon and Sian. We can never fully repay you for all your help and support.

I sincerely hope that the 50% proceeds of income made from the Mind Monsters books will, in some way, help to fill the large budget deficit that sadly still exists within the children's mental health sector.

Finally, I want to dedicate this book to my two inspiring daughters, who never fail to amaze me.

ABOUT THE AUTHOR

Julie Derrick is a busy wife and mum of two teenage girls, who juggles her time between doing what she loves most; namely, running a tight ship at home in Wales and her passion for writing and helping others.

She is also stepmother to two grown-up children and a stepgrandmother to four grandchildren.

The idea to write her Mind Monsters books came after one of Julie's own daughters was diagnosed with OCD.

Julie's mission is to try to raise awareness of child OCD and to help parents to spot early signs of it before it takes hold.

She describes her life as being hectic, but claims she wouldn't want it any other way as it helps to keep her young!

You can benefit from regular tips and updates relating to children's mental health issues by following Julie on her website, social media platforms and blog:

Facebook: **www.facebook.com/themindmonsters**

Website: **www.themindmonsters.co.uk**

Blog: **www.copywhatiuse.com**

Instagram: **www.instragram.com/julie.derrick55a**

Linked In: **www.linkedin.com/in/julie-derrick**

Twitter: **www.twitter.com/JulieDerrick17**